In the Pond

Edited by Gillian Doherty
With thanks to Dr. Margaret Rostron and Dr. John Rostron
for information about pond life

Illustrations Copyright © Mat Russell 2006.
The right of Mat Russell to be identified as the Illustrator of his Work has been asserted by
him in accordance with the Copyright Designs and Patents Act 1988.
This edition first published in 2013 by Usborne Publishing Ltd, 83-85 Saffron Hill, London
EC1N 8RT, England. www.usborne.com Copyright © 2013, 2006 Usborne Publishing Ltd. The
name Usborne and the devices ♀ 🎈 are Trade Marks of Usborne Publishing Ltd. All rights
reserved. No part of this publication may be reproduced, stored in a retrieval system, or
transmitted in any form or by any means, electronic, mechanical, photocopying, recording or
otherwise, without prior permission of the publisher. First published in America in 2013. UE.

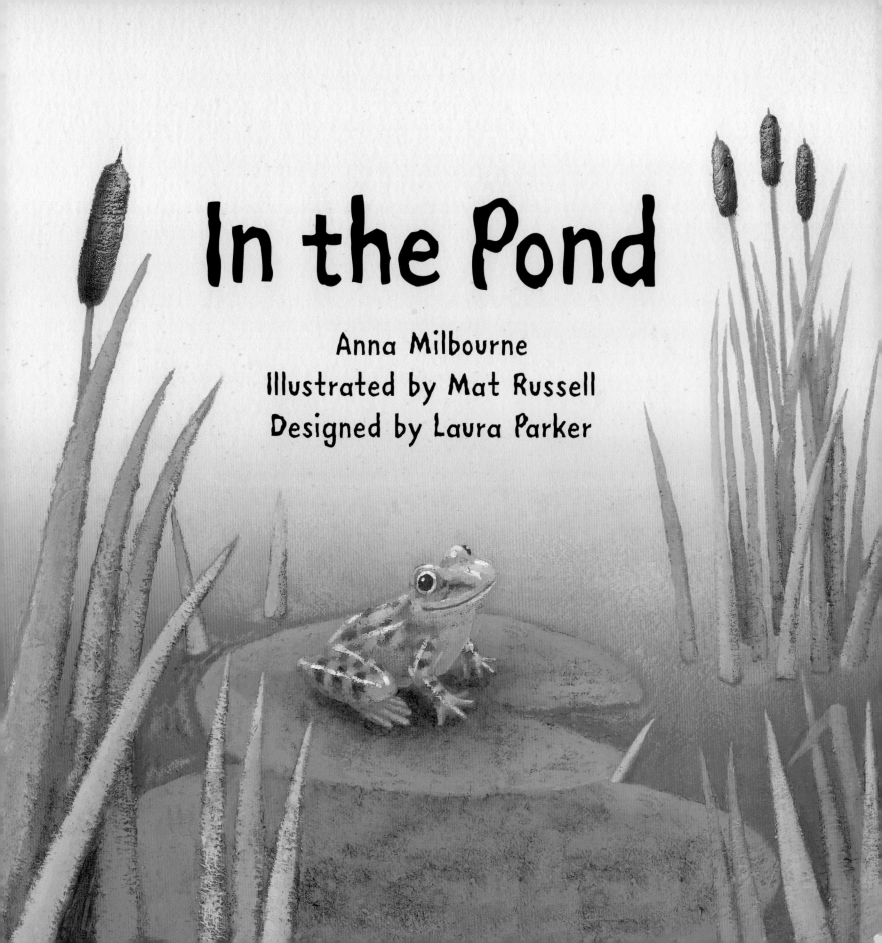

In the Pond

Anna Milbourne

Illustrated by Mat Russell

Designed by Laura Parker

Down at the pond on a bright spring day...

two swans glide gracefully along...

and ducks turn tail up,
dabbling for pondweed.

Lots of little jelly eggs
are floating in the water.

The eggs have tiny blobs inside.
What will they become?

As the days drift by,
the blobs start to grow.

They get bigger
and **bigger**.

Each one becomes a tadpole.

The tadpoles wriggle
out of their eggs...

and squiggle-swim away.

As the last little tadpole shivers free,
a huge, dark shadow looms above.

Suddenly, an enormous fish swishes down.

Its toothy jaws
gape open.

SNAP!

The little tadpole wriggles away just in time.

The days grow warmer still,
and spring slips into summer.

Shimmering dragonflies
dart around...

and a pondskater tiptoes
carefully across the water.

Over in the reeds there's a peep peep peep.

One by one, six fluffy ducklings
plop into the pond.

They paddle in a bobbing line
behind the mother duck.

Some stop to stare at butterflies...

then rush to catch back up.

Under the water,
the tadpole is changing.

He grows tiny legs
at the back and the front.

His wriggly tail
shrinks and shrinks.

Then, before you know it...

hops around,
exploring the sunlit pond.

A teeny-tiny fly flies by.

Quick as a flash, the hungry frog
rolls out his sticky tongue.

With a hop
and a splash

he dives back into the cool water.

Kicking his wide-webbed froggy feet,
he quickly swims away.

If you come back to the pond one bright spring day...

you might find lots more jelly eggs

and the frog, all grown up, singing a croaky song.